Key Numl Skills

ACTIVITY BOOK

Written by
Norman D Lock

Illustrated by
Andrew Warrington

CONTENTS

▶ Everything in its place 2
▶ Addition 6
▶ Subtraction 10
▶ Rounding up and down 14
▶ Special numbers 15
▶ Directed numbers 19
▶ Algebra 21
▶ Co-ordinates 23

Everything in its place

We can write any number you can think of, however huge, using just ten digits.

0 1 2 3 4 5 6 7 8 9

But it is **very important** to put these digits in the right place. This chart shows what the position of a number means.

MILLIONS	HUNDRED THOUSANDS	TEN THOUSANDS	THOUSANDS	HUNDREDS	TENS	UNITS
1,000,000	100,000	10,000	1000	100	10	1
3	4	5	6	7	2	8

So, **3,456,728** means **three million, four hundred and fifty-six thousand, seven hundred and twenty-eight**.

NOTICE TO BORROWERS!

The books in the library of the Exploratory Laboratory are not arranged alphabetically. Instead, each book is given a number. The books are arranged in number order, starting with 1, then 2, then 3 and so on. There are over 10,000 books in the library!

1 Imagine that you have borrowed some books and now have to put them back in place. Put the books in order, starting with the lowest number.

| 108 | 230 | 98 | 56 | 203 | 89 | 750 |
| 23 | 507 | 2999 | 570 | 19 | 809 | 65 |

Hero zero...

Zeros have to be in the right place, too. 207, 27 and 270 are very different numbers – it's the zero that makes the difference.

2 Which book comes immediately **after** each of these?

34...... 59...... 90...... 247......... 699.........

800......... 999......... 1499......... 5899.........

3 Which book comes immediately **before** each of these?

......48 ......71 ......80 ......300 2010

.........3400 ....5000 ....8550 10,000

4 The books are numbered using stickers. Last time Prof Boff left books within reach of her parrot, he pecked all the numbers off and left them lying on the table.

3 1 6 9

a Write down all the two digit numbers that can be made from these stickers in order, starting with the lowest.

b What is the greatest four digit **even** number you can make?

c What is the smallest four digit **odd** number you can make?

5 Now look at these stickers.

5 4 7 2

a Using all four digits, what is the lowest number a book could have?

b What is the greatest number it could have?

c Using **all four digits** each time, write out all the **other** numbers that a book could have. Start with the lowest and put the numbers in order.

6 Here are another four digits. Choose any three to make the nearest number you can to the ones shown here.

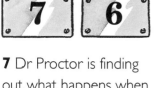

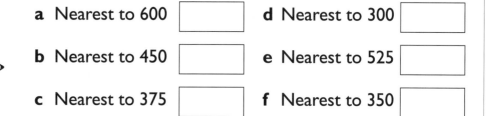

a Nearest to 600 ☐   **d** Nearest to 300 ☐

b Nearest to 450 ☐   **e** Nearest to 525 ☐

c Nearest to 375 ☐   **f** Nearest to 350 ☐

7 Dr Proctor is finding out what happens when certain numbers are added or taken away. Complete his chart by adding to or subtracting from the numbers in the blue column.

	+1	−1	+10	−10	+100	−100	+1000	−1000
1243	1244			1233		1143		
2579			2589					1579
3999		3998						
6000					6100		7000	
9999								

8 Here is part of a number line. Some of the number boxes have been filled in. Complete the remainder.

950 960 970 980 ☐ ☐ ☐ ☐ ☐ ☐

☐ ☐   ☐ ☐ ☐ ☐

9 Sadly, Dr Proctor's Extraordinary Number Exploding Machine only worked once before it broke down. Explode the other numbers as he has done below.

473 → 400 + 70 + 3

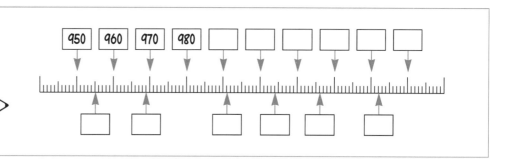

a 85 → ☐

b 136 → ☐

c 907 → ☐

d 2540 → ☐

e 14,892 → ☐

10 These labels are simply too long. Write them out as numbers instead.

a | two thousand and twelve |

b | thirty thousand, four hundred and one |

c | two hundred and one thousand and twenty |

11 Write these numbers out as words.

a 932 . . . .

b 2609 . . . .

c 48,029 . . . .

d 330,007 . . . .

12 What is the value of the underlined digit? Give your answer in numbers and words.

2<u>3</u>6 **30 (thirty)**

a 85<u>6</u> . . . .

b 1<u>2</u>58 . . . .

c <u>8</u>787 . . . .

d 19,2<u>5</u>7 . . . .

13 Use a calculator to solve these problems.

Clue: add or take away something!

a Enter 435 on your calculator. What do you have to do to change the 3 digit to a 7 without altering the 4 and 5?

. . . .

b Clear the screen. Enter 805. How can you change the 8 to a 3 without altering the 0 and the 5?

. . . .

c Clear the screen. Enter 736. How can you place a 1 in front of the 7 without putting in the whole number again?

. . . .

5

Addition

I've cleaned 143 windows. There are 89 more to clean. How many is that altogether?

To find the answer, we need to add 143 and 89. One way is to start by adding the **units**, then the **tens**, then the **hundreds**.

	H	T	U
Windows cleaned	1	4	3
Windows dirty		8	9
Altogether	2	3	2
		1	1

First we add the units: 3+9 =12.
12 means 1 ten and 2 units. We write the 2 in the units column. We **carry** the 1 ten across to the tens column.

Now we add the tens: 4+8+1 carried over =13.
13 tens means 1 hundred and 3 tens. We write the 3 in the tens column and **carry** the 1 hundred across to the hundreds column.

1+ the 1 carried over = 2.
We write the 2 in the hundreds column.

Plus point...

When you have a problem to solve, look out for key words that tell you what kind of calculation to do. If you see phrases like these, the calculation will be an **addition**.

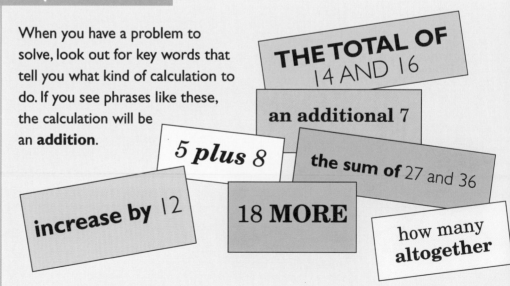

THE TOTAL OF 14 AND 16

an additional 7

5 plus 8

the sum of 27 and 36

increase by 12

18 MORE

how many altogether

1 Now try these problems. Use a separate piece of paper to work them out and write the answer after each question.

a Last year Prof Boff caused 139 explosions. This year she was more careful and only caused 76! How many is that altogether?

b Dr Proctor has 175 books on chemistry. Prof Boff has 38 more than Dr Proctor. How many does the Professor have?

c There are some long corridors in the Exploratory Laboratory! Someone has put up some helpful signs.

◀ **Cafeteria 57m**   **First Aid 68m** ▶

How far is it from the Cafeteria to the First Aid Room? ☐ m

d Prof Boff's parrot found a piece of rubber tube 85cm long and thought it was a worm. He stretched it and made it 48cm longer.

How long is it now? ☐ cm which is the same as ☐ m

When you are writing down an addition, be very careful to keep the numbers in the right columns so that you know whether they are units, tens or hundreds, and where carried numbers should be added.

Be particularly careful if you are adding **decimal** numbers. Putting decimal points in **all** the numbers helps to keep them properly lined up.

12cm + 4·5m + 6m + 2·05m   500g + 2kg + 275g + 1·3kg

Write out the numbers so that they all have the same number of decimal places. Then it is easy to add them up correctly.

0·12m	0·500kg
4·50m	2·000kg
6·00m	0·275kg
2·05m +	1·300kg +
12·67m	4·075kg

2 On a separate piece of paper, find these totals. Be careful to write the numbers in the correct columns before you add them up.

a 45p + £7 + 9p + £12 + 30p = £ ⬚

b £1·76 + 38p + £3·05 + £5 + 95p = £ ⬚

c What is the total weight of these chemicals in kilograms? ⬚ kg

 1kg  500g 350g  425g

d The drinks machine at the laboratory takes tokens instead of coins. What is the total value of Dr Proctor's tokens? £ ⬚

£1 £1 50p 50p 50p 1p 1p 20p 20p 20p 5p 10p 2p

Adding in your head

3 Do these additions in your head and write down the answers. There are some clues to help you.

a 16 add 9 ⬚

b 33 increase by 29 ⬚

c 25 with 18 extra ⬚

d 45 with an additional 28 ⬚

e the sum of 37 and 39 is ⬚

f the total of 58 and 49 is ⬚

g 8+5+3+2+5+4+7+8+6= ⬚

h 7+12+14+8+13+6+9+1= ⬚

> **CLUE**
> Remember that adding 9 is the same as adding 10 and taking 1 away.

> **CLUE**
> Numbers in an addition can be paired to make round numbers that are easy to add up.

8

48 50

Estimate the total

An **estimate** is a rough calculation that will tell you what kind of number the answer will be. Round each number up or down to the nearest 10 and then add them together to give your estimate.

4 Estimate the total of these additions.

22 + 79 =

20 + 80 = 100

a 47+33+68=   =

b 22+57+41=   =

c 198+304+248=   =

5 Now use all your addition skills to answer these questions. Work out your answers on a separate piece of paper if necessary.

a This table shows how much money Prof Boff and her team put into the chocolate biscuit fund in the second half of last year. Fill in the totals for each month.

	Jul	Aug	Sept	Oct	Nov	Dec
Prof Boff	£1·25	£2·50	£1·75	£4	£2·25	75p
Dr Proctor	£2	£1·50	£3·25	£2·50	£3	£1·25
Di Jestiff	£3·75	£1	£2·25	£5	50p	——
Gary Baldy	£1·50	£2·25	£3	£1·75	£2	£1·50
Total						

b "It cost £35·99 to feed that parrot last month!" moaned Dr Proctor. "This month it cost £3·50 more!" How much did it cost this month?

c Last month Dr Proctor weighed 79·5kg. Since then he has put on 7·25kg. What does he weigh now?

d Dr Proctor has 430ml of coffee, Prof Boff has 325ml and Jeanette S Ist has 270ml more than the Prof. How much do they have altogether?

Subtraction

I've cleaned 187 of the 232 windows. How many are left?

Taking away, **adding on** and **difference** are three different ways of thinking about subtraction.

Taking away

This means that we start with a number or an amount and **take away** from it so that we are left with less than we started with.

To find the answer, we need to take 187 away from 232.

```
H T U
    12
 1 ⨯ 12
 ⨯ ⨯ ⨯
 1 8 7 –
   4 5
```

Start with the units: 2 – 7 (2 take away 7) is not possible. Take 1 ten from the next column and exchange it for 10 units.
3 tens – 1 ten = 2 tens, so cross out the 3 in the tens column and write a 2 above it. Having taken one of the tens, you have 2 + 10 in the units column, so cross out the 2 and write 12 above it.
12 – 7 = 5   So write a 5 under the units column.

Now the tens column: 2 – 8 (2 tens take away 8 tens) is not possible. Take 1 hundred from the next column and exchange it for 10 tens. Instead of 2 hundreds in the hundreds column, there is now 1 hundred. Cross out the 2 and write a 1 above it.
In the tens column you now have 2 tens + 10 tens.
Cross out the 2 and write 12 above it.
12 – 8 = 4   So write a 4 under the tens column.

Now the hundreds column: 1 – 1 = 0   As this is the last column, don't write 0 at the bottom. We don't start numbers with a zero.

Signs of subtraction...

Here are some more key words to look out for. When you see them, you need to do a subtraction to solve the problem.

TAKE AWAY 7   remove 4
the difference between 25 and 17
35 minus 18   decrease by 12
DEDUCT 14   8 **LESS**   14 fewer than 36   subtract 23

1 Work out these subtractions on a separate piece of paper and write your answers in the boxes.

I've spent £3·24 on my lunch and given the waiter a £5 note. How much change will I get?

a Prof Boff has to measure the height of 5000 plants. She has done 1807. How many more does she have to do?

b Yesterday the parrot had 9020 red feathers. Then he walked into Dr Proctor's wind tunnel by mistake and lost 359 of them. How many red feathers does he have now?

c Between 9.30am and 4.30pm the scientists at the Exploratory Laboratory drank 307 cups of coffee. They drank 149 in the morning. How many did they drink in the afternoon?

Adding on

Another way of **subtracting** is to **add on** from the smaller number.

From £3·24 add on **6p** to round up to the nearest 10p +£0·06
From £3·30 add on **70p** to round up to the nearest pound +£0·70
From £4·00 add on **£1·00** to bring the total to £5·00 +£1·00

The change is £1·76. That is how much you have to add £1·76
to £3·24 to make £5·00.

2 Use **adding on** to find the answers to these problems. One has been done for you.

200 − 38 = 38 — **+2** → = 40 — **+60** → = 100 — **+100** → = 200 **= 162**

a 300 − 63 = 63 — **+** → = ... — **+** → = ... — **+** → = ... = [ ]

b 450 − 176 = 176 — **+** → = ... — **+** → = ... — **+** → = ... = [ ]

c 1000 − 217 = 217 — **+** → = ... — **+** → = ... — **+** → = ... = [ ]

3 Use **adding on** to find the answers to these problems. Work them out on a separate piece of paper and write your answers in the boxes.

a Nawaz has used 175ml of water from a 500ml bottle. How much does he have left?

b Prof Boff has spent £4·28 on a bell for her parrot. She paid with a £10 note. How much change did she get?

c Dr Proctor's wind tunnel experiments lasted $1\frac{1}{4}$ hours. He spent 36 minutes rescuing the parrot. How much time was left for experiments?

Difference

We can also think of subtraction not as **taking away** but as **comparing** two things to find the **difference** between them.

This ruler is 30cm long and this one is 45cm. What is the difference in their lengths?

The difference in lengths is 15cm or 0·15m

4 Work out these problems on a separate sheet of paper and write the answers here.

a Prof Boff is comparing the scientists in the laboratory. Nawaz Janeer is 1·73m tall. Di Jestiff is 1·59m in height. What is the difference in their heights?

b A can holds 1 litre and 25ml (1·025 litres) of water. A bottle holds 485ml. How much less does the bottle hold than the can?

Check point...

To check your answer when you are taking away, all you have to do is to **add** your answer to the number you took away. The result should be the number you started with.

205
85 −
120

85
120+
205

Subtraction in your head

It is useful to be able to subtract in your head. You need to be good at subtracting small numbers, so that you know $6 - 3 = 3$, for example.

5 Use all your skills to work out these answers in your head.

a 100 $\xrightarrow{-15}$ $\square$ $\xrightarrow{-30}$ $\square$ $\xrightarrow{-9}$ $\square$ $\xrightarrow{-20}$ $\square$

b 325 $\xrightarrow{-\square}$ 299 $\xrightarrow{-\square}$ 260 $\xrightarrow{-61}$ $\square$ $\xrightarrow{-\square}$ 89

c 36 remove 9 = $\square$ **e** 400 decrease by 37 = $\square$

d 72 deduct 38 = $\square$ **f** 29 fewer than 75 = $\square$

6 Each of these clocks is fast. In your head work out the time that each clock should be showing.

a | 20.05 | 20 minutes fast   Correct time $\boxed{}$

b | 8.30 | 45 minutes fast   Correct time $\boxed{}$

c | 2.55 | 15 minutes fast   Correct time $\boxed{}$

7 Use all your subtraction skills to find the answers to these problems.

Fill in the missing numbers in these subtractions.

a
```
  8□3
 □8□ -
 ───
  507
```

b
```
  735
  5□9 -
 ───
  □8□
```

c
```
 □24□
 46□3 -
 ───
 2□67
```

d
```
  9□□5
 247□ -
 ───
 □086
```

e Katya, the youngest scientist at the Laboratory, is 15. Prof S Oare, the oldest, is 83. He has worked there for 56 years. Before that he lived in Peru. How long did he live in Peru? $\boxed{}$

How much older than Katya is he? $\boxed{}$

Rounding up and down

How many ants have you let out?

Sometimes we do not need to know the **exact** number of something but only the **approximate** number. That is a number that has been rounded up or down, for example, to the nearest 10, 100, or 1000.

About 5,000!

Here is a useful rule for whenever you need to give an approximate number.

If a digit is **under 5**, round it down.
If a digit is **5 or more**, round it up.

1 Prof Boff is trying to find out how far she walks each day. Fill in the table showing the distance from Prof Boff's desk to other parts of the laboratory.

Place	Exact distance from Prof Boff's desk	Rounded to the nearest 10m	Rounded to the nearest 100m
Cafeteria	**784m**		
Toilets	**216m**		
Dr Proctor	**848m**		

2 Prof Boff has worked out how much time she has spent on her feet on three days of this week. Round the times to the nearest **hour**.

a Monday: 4 hrs 5 mins   ☐ hrs

b Tuesday: 7 hrs 50 mins   ☐ hrs

c Wednesday: 10 hrs 30 mins   ☐ hrs

3 Prof Boff has decided that other people should come to **her**, but now her office is never empty! Fill in this chart to show the number of visitors she has in one month.

Reason for visit	Exact number of people	Rounded to the nearest 10	Rounded to nearest 100	Rounded to nearest 1000
Moaning about Dr Proctor	**5317**			
Moaning from Dr Proctor	**9086**			
Came to talk to parrot	**2683**			
Important business	**1501**			

Special numbers

Factors and prime numbers

The factors of a number are those numbers that divide exactly into that number.

The factors of **30** are: **1 2 3 5 6 10 15 30**

All those numbers divide exactly into 30.

Some numbers only have **two** factors. They are called **prime numbers**. Their factors are the number itself and 1.

23 is a prime number. It can only be divided by 1 and 23. The number **1** is **not a prime number**.

Multiples

These numbers are some of the multiples of 3.

The first few multiples of 4 are: 4, 8, 12, 16, 20…
But multiples don't stop there! They can be much bigger numbers.

1 Dr Proctor has become very interested in Eratosthenes. He was a Greek mathematician who lived over two thousand years ago. He worked out a way to find all the prime numbers under 100. Follow the instructions opposite. All the numbers that are left are prime numbers. How many are there under 100?

Cross out all the multiples of 2 except 2.
Cross out all the multiples of 3 except 3.
Cross out all the multiples of 5 except 5.
Cross out all the multiples of 7 except 7.
Cross out 1.

1	2	3	4	5	6	7	8	9	10
11	12	13	14	15	16	17	18	19	20
21	22	23	24	25	26	27	28	29	30
31	32	33	34	35	36	37	38	39	40
41	42	43	44	45	46	47	48	49	50
51	52	53	54	55	56	57	58	59	60
61	62	63	64	65	66	67	68	69	70
71	72	73	74	75	76	77	78	79	80
81	82	83	84	85	86	87	88	89	90
91	92	93	94	95	96	97	98	99	100

PRIME NUMBERS

2 What is the nearest prime number to each of the following?

a 25 ...... **b** 40 ...... **c** 65 ...... **d** 80 ......

3 Find two different prime numbers whose sum is equal to each of these even numbers. Remember that 1 is not a prime number.

a 10 = ☐ + ☐   **d** 36 = ☐ + ☐

b 12 = ☐ + ☐   **e** 48 = ☐ + ☐

c 34 = ☐ + ☐   **f** 60 = ☐ + ☐

Will it work for **all even** numbers? ☐

4 Draw four more different rectangles on the grid to show the pairs of factors of 36. Each rectangle should contain 36 squares.

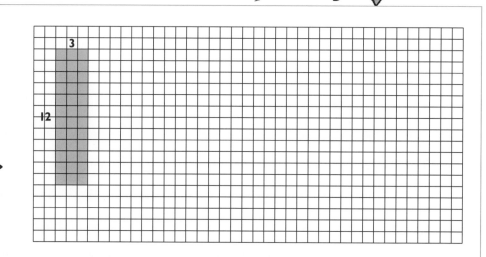

a Write out the pairs of factors of 36.

×	×	×	×	×

b Write the factors of 36 in order. Start with the lowest.

☐ ☐ ☐ ☐ ☐ ☐ ☐ ☐ ☐

Square numbers

The quick way of finding square numbers is to multiply a number by itself. We call this **squaring a number**. There is a quick way of writing it, too.

$$8 \times 8 = 64$$
$$8^2 = 64$$

Square roots

The number that is multiplied by itself to form a **square number** is called the **square root** of that square.

Square roots are written like this: $\sqrt{49} = 7$

Here are the first 10 square numbers and their square roots.

Square number	1	4	9	16	25	36	49	64	81	100
Square root	1	2	3	4	5	6	7	8	9	10

5 Use the clues on the scraps of paper to find the mystery numbers.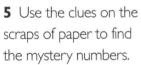

a
square number
it is odd
< 50, > 20
7 is a factor

b
> 50, < 90
it is an even
multiple of 8
24 is a factor

c
prime number
< 40 with 2 digits.
If you double it and
take away 9 you get a
square number

d
it is even
< 79
5, 4 and 3 are all
factors

1 square × 1 square
× 1 square = 1 cube

2 × 2 × 2 = 8 cubes

3 × 3 × 3 = 27 cubes

The numbers of small cubes needed to make large cubes are called **cube numbers**. The quick way of finding cube numbers is to multiply a number by itself and then by itself again.

We can write this in a quick way, too. $4 \times 4 \times 4 = 64$ $4^3 = 64$

The number that is multiplied by itself and by itself again is called the **cubed root** of the final number. The cubed root of 1000 is 10. A cube made of 1000 small cubes would have 10 cubes along one edge.

There is a special way of writing cubed roots, too. $\sqrt[3]{27} = 3$

Here are the first ten cube numbers and their cubed roots.

Cube number	1	8	27	64	125	216	343	512	729	1000
Cube root	1	2	3	4	5	6	7	8	9	10

6 Prof Boff and her team are doing some investigations into cubes. Complete their chart and see if you can spot any number patterns developing.

Length of cube sides	1	2	3	4	5	6	7	8	9	10
Number of small cubes used	1	8	27	64	125					
How many more small cubes used this time?	+7	+19	+37	+61						
How many more added than last time?		12	18	24						

7 Find the answers to these problems. The one below has been done for you.

$3^2 + \sqrt{25} =$
$9 + 5 \quad = 14$

a $2^3 - \sqrt{49} =$ ☐ = ☐

b $\sqrt[3]{64} + 6^2 =$ ☐ = ☐

c $3^3 - \sqrt{100} =$ ☐ = ☐

d $\sqrt{81} + 4^2 =$ ☐ = ☐

Directed numbers

Here is a game using directed numbers that is very popular in the Exploratory Laboratory.

Positive numbers and negative numbers are called **directed numbers** because we can use them to count **in two different directions** from zero.

negative numbers   positive numbers

‾10 ‾9 ‾8 ‾7 ‾6 ‾5 ‾4 ‾3 ‾2 ‾1 0 ⁺1 ⁺2 ⁺3 ⁺4 ⁺5 ⁺6 ⁺7 ⁺8 ⁺9 ⁺10

You will need:
- Dice of two different colours (say black and red)
- A small counter for each player
- The number line above

Rules

Start at zero. Throw both dice together. The number on the black die moves you forwards (to the right) in a positive direction. The number on the red die moves you backwards (to the left) in a negative direction.

It doesn't matter which move you make first. For example, say you throw a black 6 and a red 3. We can write that as ⁺6 and ‾3. On the line below you can see that whether you move ⁺6 and then ‾3 or ‾3 and then ⁺6, you still end up at ⁺3.

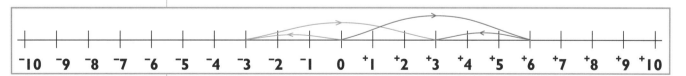

‾10 ‾9 ‾8 ‾7 ‾6 ‾5 ‾4 ‾3 ‾2 ‾1 0 ⁺1 ⁺2 ⁺3 ⁺4 ⁺5 ⁺6 ⁺7 ⁺8 ⁺9 ⁺10

Play the game with a partner. The winner is the first person to move off the end of the line at either end. Good luck!

1 This table shows the first four throws made by five scientists playing the same game. Work out where each one finishes. Jeanette's final position has already been worked out.

Turns	Jeanette S 1st		Prof Boff		Dr Proctor		Alec Trishan		N Janeer	
	Black	Red	Black	Red	Black	Red	Black	Red	Black	Red
1st	4	1	3	3	1	5	6	1	2	6
2nd	2	3	2	5	3	4	4	3	5	4
3rd	2	5	4	1	6	5	4	4	6	1
4th	6	4	1	4	2	3	2	3	3	5
Finish	+1									

2 Dr Proctor is worried that cold weather will affect his experiments. Use his record of dawn temperatures last week to put the days in order, starting with the coldest dawn and moving to the warmest.

Monday: ⁻3°C
Tuesday: 0°C
Wednesday: ⁺1°C
Thursday: ⁻1°C
Friday: ⁺2°C

Coldest dawn . . . .

. . . .

. . . .

. . . .

Warmest dawn . . . .

3 Last week Dr Proctor made a record of the temperature when he arrived at work and the temperature at midday. Complete his chart.

Temperature at 9.00am	Temperature at noon	Change in temperature
⁺5°C	°C	Fall of 6°C
⁻4°C	°C	Rise of 2°C
⁻3°C	⁺7°C	
⁺2°C	⁻6°C	
°C	⁻3°C	Rise of 4°C

At the Exploratory Laboratory a silly argument has begun about whose desk has the highest pile of paper. Prof Boff claims that her pile is the ideal size, so the height of her pile should be 0. Everyone else's papers can be measured as directed numbers from 0.

4 Look at the chart.
a If Prof Boff's pile of papers is 46cm tall, write in the heights of the other piles.
b Of course, Dr Proctor protests. Write the other piles as directed numbers if **his** pile is taken as 0.

	⁻7 Nawaz	⁻4 Jeanette	0 Prof Boff	⁺5 Alec	⁺9 Dr Proctor
Heights of piles with Prof Boff's pile as zero			46cm		
Directed numbers for heights of piles with Dr Proctor's pile as zero					0

Algebra

Prof Boff is on the trail of some mysterious series of numbers. By writing number clues between each of the numbers, she can usually work out what the next three numbers should be.

1 See if you can find the clues that will help you solve these mystery numbers and write the next three in the series. One has been done for you already.

1, (+1) 2, (+2) 4, (+3) 7, (+4) 11, (+5) 16, (+6) 22, (+7) 29

a 5, (...) 11, (...) 17, (...) 23, (...) 29, (...) ..., (...) ..., (...) ...

b 3, (...) 13, (...) 22, (...) 30, (...) 37, (...) ..., (...) ..., (...) ...

c 40, (...) 39, (...) 37, (...) 34, (...) 30, (...) ..., (...) ..., (...) ...

2 Now Dr Proctor has some more number puzzles for Prof Boff. Work them out in your head and then write down the answers.

a When he multiplies it by 3, he gets 27!

b When he divides it by 4, he gets 12!

c When he doubles it and deducts 1, he gets 15!

d When he squares it and adds 1, he gets 50!

4 + 3 x 2 = 14

4 + 3 x 2 = 10

Using brackets

How can there be **two** answers? It depends which part you do first. If you add 4 and 3 and multiply the result by 2, you get 14. If you multiply 3 by 2 and add 4 to the result, you get 10. To be clear, we put **brackets around the part that should be done first**.

3 Do these problems in your head and write down the answers. Be careful to do the parts in brackets first.

a (5+2) x 4 = ☐

b 5 + (2x4) = ☐

c 19 − (4x2) = ☐

d (19−4) x 2 = ☐

Letters standing for numbers

In algebra, we can use letters to stand for, or represent, numbers. For example, **a** could stand for the number 8 and **c** stand for the number 4.

$$a = 8 \quad c = 4$$

We can use **a** and **c** just as we would numbers.

$$a + c = 12 \quad a - c = 4 \quad 2a = 16 \quad a^2 = 64 \quad \sqrt[3]{a} = 2 \quad \frac{a}{2} = 4$$

Sometimes we need to work out what a letter stands for.

If $d + 4 = 9$ If $5e = 30$
then $d = 5$ then $e = 6$
because $5 + 4 = 9$ because $5 \times 6 = 30$

4 Find out what these letters stand for.

a $w + 6 = 14$ $w = \boxed{}$ d $3t = 27$ $t = \boxed{}$

b $21 - u = 15$ $u = \boxed{}$ e $d^2 = 81$ $d = \boxed{}$

c $7 + s = 13$ $s = \boxed{}$ f $n^2 - 1 = 35$ $n = \boxed{}$

Dr Proctor has built a Number Crunching Machine. He feeds numbers into it and the machine spits out new numbers at the other end.

It is the boxes that change the numbers. To begin with, the machine is programmed to **multiply by 2** and then **take away 1**.

5 Dr Proctor has been careless about recording what happens when he feeds in a new number or changes the boxes. Complete his chart.

Box 1	Box 2	Box 1	Box 2	Box 1	Box 2	Box 1	Box 2	Box 1	Box 2
x2	−1	x3	÷2	+1	x3				
In	Out	In	Out	In	Out	In	Out	In	Out
4	7	6		5		4	10	2	3
5		10		7		7	16	3	8
	15	16			45	13	28	6	35
20				60	20		9		8
	35	8			81		14		99

Co-ordinates

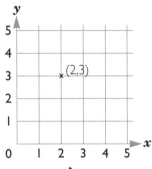

A grid like the one on the left can help us to describe the position of a point. The line along the bottom (the horizontal) is called the **x axis**. The line up the side (the vertical) is called the **y axis**.
It is the **lines** of the grid that are numbered, **not the spaces**.

To describe where something is on the grid, think of it as being at the point where a line from the **x axis** and a line from the **y axis** cross.

Always write the **x number first** and the **y number second** and put a comma between them. These pairs of numbers are called **co-ordinates** or **ordered pairs**.

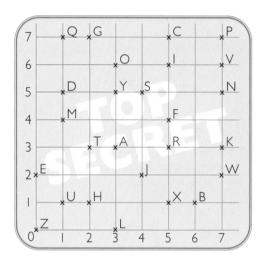

News of Dr Proctor's Number Crunching Machine has reached two scientists from a laboratory nearby. They plan to steal it. To send secret messages, each carries a copy of this code card.

I Decode this message from one of the rival scientists to the other. He has put vertical lines to separate the words.

(1,4) (0,2) (0,2)(2,3) | (3,3) (2,3) | (1,4) (5,6) (1,5) (7,5) (5,6) (2,7) (2,1) (2,3) |

. . . .

(2,3) (0,2) (3,0) (3,0) | (7,5) (3,6) (6,1) (3,6) (1,5) (3,5) | (6,1) (5,3) (5,6) (7,5) (2,7) |

. . . .

(5,4) (3,6) (3,6) (1,5) | (5,4) (3,6) (5,3) | (7,7) (3,3) (5,3) (5,3) (3,6) (2,3)

. . . .

2 Write this warning message in code.

KEEP   YOUR   CODE
CARD   SAFE

. . . .

. . . .

23

3 Mark on the grid the co-ordinates below and join them up in the order that they are written here. What letters do they make?

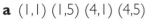

a (1,1) (1,5) (4,1) (4,5)

b (6,1) (6,5) (8,3) (10,5) (10,1)

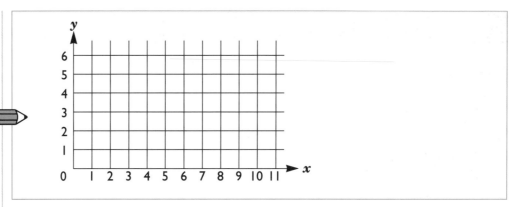

In the example below, the **x axis** represents **tens** and the **y axis** represents **units**. You will notice that the **y axis** stops at 9 but the **x axis** has an arrow to show it can go on for ever.

On this grid it is possible to represent numbers. For example, **8** would be (0,8), meaning no tens and 8 units. The number **24** would be (2,4), meaning 2 tens and 4 units.

This grid has been used to show the multiples of 8. You can see they form a pattern.

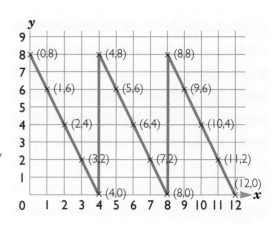

4 Use this grid to find the co-ordinates for the multiples of 7 and link them to show what kind of pattern they make.

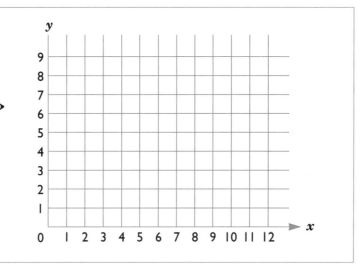

(7,2)(2,1)(3,6)'(4,5) | (3,3) | (5,7)(3,0)(0,2)(7,6)(0,2)(5,3) | (6,1)(3,6)(3,5) | (2,3)(2,1)(0,2)(7,5) ?

24